PROJECT MONARCH

ATED BY PAT MILLS & JOHN HIGGINS

GREYSUIT

PROJECT MONARCH

PAT MILLS
Writer

JOHN HIGGINS
Artist

Creative Director and CEO: Jason Kingsley
Chief Technical Officer: Chris Kingsley
2000 AD Editor in Chief: Matt Smith
Graphic Novels Editor: Keith Richardson
Graphic Design: Simon Parr & Luke Preece
Reprographics: Kathryn Symes
Original Commissioning Editor: Matt Smith

Published by Rebellion, Riverside House, Osney Mead, Oxford, UK. OX2 0ES
www.rebellion.co.uk

ISBN: 978-1-907519-82-6
Printed in Malta by Gutenberg Press
Manufactured in the EU by LPPS Ltd., Wellingborough, NN8 3PJ, UK.
First published: January 2011
10 9 8 7 6 5 4 3 2 1

Printed on FSC Accredited Paper

A CIP catalogue record for this book is available from the British Library.

For information on other *2000 AD* graphic novels, or if you have any comments on this book, please email books@2000ADonline.com

To find out more about *2000 AD*, visit www.2000ADonline.com

HEROES AND VILLAINS

Mach One – a super-powered secret agent – was the number one character in *2000 AD's* first three critical months. The reason why he died was not because the readers grew tired of him, but rather because the standard of later stories and art was often poor compared to the rest of *2000 AD*. It requires more effort to write and draw a *successful* modern-day comic strip than a story set five hundred years in the future.

Enter *Greysuit*, a *Mach One* for the 21st century. The key to his popularity is an obvious one which he has in common with all the best fictional secret agents: the characters and incidents portrayed are largely based on real life. Thus the late, great artist John Hicklenton gave me my core plot: the authentic story of criminals who discover appalling and incriminating photos of a government minister in a bank vault they've broken into. Johnny's source had told him about this crime some years before the film *The Bank Job,* which pursues a different but comparable theme. The big fear for the robbers was the "Greysuits" coming after them if they dealt with the pervert in the traditional East End gangster manner. That's why they left the photos on the floor for the cops to find instead. As "Greysuit" was the authentic name used by the criminal fraternity for a British secret agent, it had to be the name of my hero.

Thus the inciting opening incident set in the Middle East - teenagers arrested and beaten up for breakdancing – is sadly all too real. The later assassination on an Indian reservation was inspired by a visit to the Hopi Indian reservations. I sat in the office of the Hopi Minister of the Interior as he talked to a New Age friend of mine who was desperate to help the Indians as part of her spiritual quest. He looked her straight in the eye and said, "The best thing white people can do to help us is... to go away." Good advice which needed to be recorded. A visit to Sarajevo shortly after the war there inspired the car chase through that city. And information about the appalling Arizona Market in Bosnia and the sinister Project Monarch can be found on the web.

But the ultimate hero in *Greysuit* is based on a man you're unlikely to read about elsewhere called Fouladvand. He really was the voice of John Wayne and Gary Cooper in classic cowboy films shown in his country; he was the leader of a resistance movement; and the Greysuits did not appreciate his satellite broadcasts and put a stop to them. I watched some of his phone-ins and laughed out loud at his courageous and quick-witted rejoinders to critics who would call him, threatening his life. The reason why Fouladvand and his spectacular resistance movement has been completely ignored by *all* sections of the British press, as well as by novelists, is not an oversight. It's because it would challenge the orthodox media model of the Middle East imposed on us. I wish I could have done this great man more justice. Tragically and inevitably, Fouladvand was recently captured by his enemies and is in prison or dead.

The success of *Greysuit* confirms that stories based on real life heroes and villains can work. John Higgins artwork captures the essence of the character so well and I hope to team up with him on a sequel. After all, there is unfinished business for Greysuit and if there aren't many heroes out there anymore, there is surely a long list of real-life bad guys to inspire us.

Pat Mills November 2010

PROJECT MONARCH

Script: Pat Mills
Art: John Higgins
Colours: J.H. & S.J. Hurst
Lettering: Ellie De Ville

Originally published in *2000 AD* Progs 1540-1549

...RYONE WENT UP ...MOUNTAIN ON ...DAY OF REST.

SOME WENT THERE TO FIND A SECRET PLACE TO MAKE OUT WITH THEIR GIRLFRIENDS. SOME WENT THERE TO DRINK ALCOHOL.

OTHERS WENT THERE TO **DANCE**.

ALL WERE BREAKING THE LAW. IF THEY WERE CAUGHT, THERE WERE SEVERE PENALTIES.

...E MET **THE FOX** AT THE WATERFALL ...HALFWAY UP THE MOUNTAIN. HE ...SE IT BECAUSE THERE WAS LESS ...THAN MEETING IN THE CITY.

...ND THE MOUNTAIN ...AD SEVERAL EXITS.

THE FOX WAS AN IMPORTANT MEMBER OF THE GOVERNMENT. THIS WAS WHY HE LOOKED SO UNIMPORTANT.

IN PUBLIC, HIS COUNTRY WAS PART OF 'THE AXIS OF EVIL'. IN PRIVATE, IT WAS BUSINESS AS USUAL.

HOW MANY CHALLENGER TANKS DO YOU WANT?

THE MORE YOU BUY, THE CHEAPER THE PRICE.

VIOLENT HOLLYWOOD [FIL]MS **MAY** BE VERY POPULAR [OVE]R THERE, JOHN, BUT WE DON'T [W]ANT YOU CARRYING OUT YOUR **OWN** VERSION.

YOU'RE A **GREYSUIT**, NOT RAMBO.

YES, SIR.

LEAVE THAT SORT OF THING TO THE AMERICANS, HMM? IT'S NOT VERY **BRITISH**.

I UNDERSTAND, SIR. THANK YOU, SIR.

HE'S LYING.

[I]S **DOCTOR** [G]**REEN** STILL [B]USY?

SHE'S JUST FINISHED GIVING A **PRIMAL**.

ASK HER IF SHE'LL COME OVER FOR A CHAT.

AND LET'S HAVE A LOOK AT HIS FILE. I WANT TO SEE WHAT HAPPENED ON HIS PREVIOUS MISSION...

'THE MARBLE ARCH SAFETY DEPOSIT CENTRE ROBBERY, SIR. SIX TARGETS. YOU ASSIGNED **ZIL** TO TERMINATE THREE OF THEM, **BLAKE** THE OTHER THREE.'

'AH, YES. UNUSUAL FOR US TO BE INTERESTED IN **BANK ROBBERS**.'

THEY DISCOVERED COMPROMISING PHOTOS OF THE **MINISTER** WHEN THEY BROKE INTO HIS PRIVATE DEPOSIT BOX.

I REMEMBER.

I WANTED TO **WASH MY HANDS** AFTER TOUCHING THEM...

MOST REGRETTABLE.

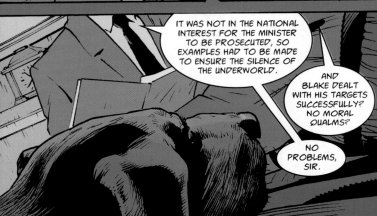

IT WAS NOT IN THE NATIONAL INTEREST FOR THE MINISTER TO BE PROSECUTED, SO EXAMPLES HAD TO BE MADE TO ENSURE THE SILENCE OF THE UNDERWORLD.

AND BLAKE DEALT WITH HIS TARGETS SUCCESSFULLY? NO MORAL QUALMS?

NO PROBLEMS, SIR.

GOOD. ALTHOUGH I HAVE TO SAY EVEN I FIND THESE PHOTOS **DEEPLY OFFENSIVE**...

AFTER ALL...

... THEY'RE JUST KIDS.

THEY'RE JUST KIDS...

ONCE A YEAR, AT THE SAME TIME, HE HAD THE **DREAM**...

AT SCHOOL, HE WAS AN OUTSTANDING ATHLETE BUT HIS MOTHER COULD NO LONGER AFFORD THE FEES.

AND THEN **DUNSTAN WOOD**, A GOVERNOR AND OLD BOY OF THE SCHOOL, CAME DOWN ONE SPORTS DAY.

HE EXPLAINED HOW HIS GOVERNMENT DEPARTMENT WOULD PAY FOR HIS EDUCATION IN RETURN FOR HIS ENLISTING AS AN AGENT.

AFTER SCHOOL, HE SPENT FOUR YEARS IN THE ARMY.

THEN 'THE OLD MAN' TOOK HIM TO THE PORTSTOCK INSTITUTE OF HUMAN RELATIONS FOR 'FURTHER TRAINING'.

THE INSTITUTE WAS SET UP AFTER WORLD WAR ONE, UNDER THE DIRECTION OF THE BRITISH ARMY BUREAU OF PSYCHOLOGICAL WARFARE.

IT STUDIED THE EFFECTS OF POST-TRAUMATIC STRESS ON SOLDIERS WHO SURVIVED THE TRENCHES.

SHELL SHOCK. AMNESIA. PSYCHOSIS.

PORTSTOCK INSTITUTE

BUT WHAT TOOK PLACE INSIDE, HE COULD NEVER REMEMBER.

JUST THE MEMORY OF A WOMAN IN WHITE. SHE FILLED HIM WITH RAGE AND FEAR, BUT HE HAD NO IDEA WHO SHE WAS OR WHAT SHE DID TO HIM.

UNTIL NOW.

AFTER THE DREAM, HE ALWAYS AWOKE WITH A MASSIVE HANGOVER.

IT WAS HIS BODY'S REMINDER OF HOW THEY HAD DRUGGED HIM.

'HAPPY ANNIVERSARY, JOHN.'

DRINKING LITRES OF WATER CLEARED THE TOXINS.

...THE **MINISTER** WAS OPENING THE KINVALLA HOME FOR CHILDREN WITH EMOTIONAL BEHAVIOUR DISORDERS.

THE HOME OFFERS TAILOR-MADE CARE PACKAGES FOR EACH CHILD: QUAD-BIKING, HORSE-RIDING, ROCK-CLIMBING, SAILING AND CAMPING.

CHILDREN ARE OUR FUTURE.

SANYO

I HA VOLUNTEERED HELP THEM ON SO OF THEIR ADVENTURES

AFTER HE SPARED THE DON'S LIFE, HE HELD ONTO THE PHOTOS OF THE MINISTER. BUT SOMETHING MADE HIM HIDE THEM, FORGET ABOUT THEM...

... UNTIL THAT DAY ON BREAKDANCE MOUNTAIN WHEN HIS CONDITIONING BROKE DOWN AGAIN.

...'S TO THE ...O-BUG HE HAD ...EN ON HARDY'S COLLAR, HE NOW ... EVERYTHING.

HE KNEW THE WOMAN WAS DOCTOR GREEN, AND THAT SHE SPECIALISED IN TRAUMA-BASED MIND CONTROL.

HE READ EVERYTHING HE COULD FIND ON THE SUBJECT.

THEY HAD MANY TECHNIQUES: FEAR. DRUGS. ULTRASONICS. THEY COULD USE A CHIP ON YOUR SHOULDER OR PUT ONE IN YOUR HEAD.

THEY CREATED AMNESIC BARRIERS THAT SEALED MEMORIES FROM THE CONSCIOUS MIND SO YOU BECAME WHO THEY WANTED YOU TO BE...

HIS NAME WAS ZILENSKY — NICKNAMED 'ZIL', AFTER THE RUSSIAN BLACK LIMOUSINES.

HE HAD OTHER NICK-NAMES AS WELL, BUT ANYONE WHO CALLED HIM 'SILENCER OF THE LAMBS' OR 'THE BAD SHEPHERD' USUALLY ENDED UP DEAD.

ZIL DID NOT APPRECIATE JOKES ABOUT HIS PAST.

THE GUARDS CHECKING FOR WEAPONS DIDN'T KNOW **DELTA-CLASS AGENTS** WERE **LIVING** WEAPONS.

LIKE THE REST OF THE ASSASSINS CREATED BY PROJECT MONARCH.

ALPHA: USUALLY LONE 'CRAZIES' WHO HAD NO IDEA THEY HAD BEEN PROGRAMMED TO KILL.

BETA: 'SLEEPERS' ACTIVATED TO KILL, THEN COMMIT SUICIDE.

GAMMA: AGENTS CONTROLLED BY BRAIN IMPLANTS, LASERS OR OTHER TECHNOLOGICAL MEANS.

THETA: AGENTS WHO USED OCCULT METHODS OF EXECUTION, CONTROLLED BY PSYCHICS AND TELEPATHS.

OMEGA: THE ONLY ASSASSINS ABOVE DELTA. NO ONE TALKED ABOUT OMEGA MEN.

DED TO KILL
GHTS. HE WAS
D TO ELIMINATE
TS IN THE DARK.

HE FELT THE USUAL FIGHT OR
FLIGHT RESPONSES: COLD
SWEAT, TREMORS, BLOOD
AND ADRENALIN RUSH.

THEY BOOSTED HIS BODY
FROM 10% NORMAL HUMAN
EFFICIENCY TO 100% EFFICIENCY.

HIS EYES BECAME LIKE A CAT'S,
AMPLIFYING LIGHT, NARROWING
AND DEFOCUSING TO ALSO
INCREASE HIS PERIPHERAL VISION.

HIS NOSTRILS PICKED UP THE
AFTERSHAVE SCENT
SIGNATURES OF THE GUNMEN.

HIS HEARING AMPLIFIED
SO HE COULD HEAR
THEIR HEARTBEATS.

HIS FISTS DID
THE REST.

LATERAL BODY AWARENESS —
THE SIXTH SENSE — TOOK CARE
OF ANY UNEXPECTED THREATS.

YOU
KILLED
DRAGAN!

HE KNEW WHEN SOMEONE HAD ENTERED HIS APARTMENT. THE USUAL HAIR ACROSS THE DOOR HAD BEEN MOVED SLIGHTLY.

HE NORMALLY WORE WOOLLEN SUITS TO AVOID THE SOUND MADE BY CLOTHES RUSTLING.

HE HAD PERIPHERAL BODY SENSES. HE COULD FEEL WHEN SOMEONE WAS CLOSE BY.

SO COULD ZIL.

DELTA AGENTS' ADRENALINE LEVELS WERE FAR ABOVE ORDINARY HUMANS.

IT FELT TO BLAKE LIKE BEING IN A CAR AT MAXIMUM REVS ALL THE TIME.

DRIVING IN FIFTH GEAR.

AT 150 MPH.

IT WAS THE MOS EXHILARATING F IN THE WORLD.

KILLING BECA A PLEASURE.

THEY WERE TRAINED TO USE HOUSEHOLD ITEMS AS WEAPONS.

NEITHER FELT FEAR, BECAUSE THE TRAUMA OF THEIR PRIMALS HAD RELEASED LARGE QUANTITIES OF **NEUROPEPTIDES**...

... THE BRAIN CHEMICALS THAT CREATE **COURAGE**.

BUT IT WAS NECESSARY FOR THEM TO KILL TO BLOCK OUT THE MEMORY OF THEIR PRIMALS...

... FREQUENTLY.

THEY WERE ADDICTED TO **DEATH**. IT WAS THEIR DRUG OF CHOICE.

THEY COULD PROJECT THEIR RAGE AND HATRED ONTO THEIR OPPONENT...

... AND FEEL SOME RELEASE.

THIS WAS WHY BLAKE FELT LIKE HE WAS CONSTANTLY DRIVING IN THE FAST LANE.

WITHOUT A KILLING, THEY WOULD 'OVER-REV'...

... AND BURN OUT.

IN THEIR MINDS, IT WAS DOCTOR GREEN OR DUNSTAN WOOD THEY WERE ATTACKING.

OR IN ZIL'S CASE, HIS MOTHER.

IT WAS **HOMICIDE** THERAPY.

IT SWEPT OUT THE DETRITUS IN THEIR HEADS.

ONLY THEY WOULD NEVER BE CLEAN AGAIN.

MR BLAKE...? SHALL I DO YOU NOW, SIR?

HAD A BIT OF A PARTY, SIR?

SARAJEVO, BOSNIA:

NOW BLAKE HAD BEGUN TO REMEMBER, THERE WERE **MANY** QUESTIONS HE NEEDED ANSWERS TO.

THE DEPARTMENT HAD PAID FOR HIS PUBLIC SCHOOL EDUCATION AFTER HIS MOTHER RAN OUT OF MONEY.

BUT HIS FATHER **HAD** LEFT THEM WELL PROVIDED FOR UNTIL HER SHARE PORTFOLIO MYSTERIOUSLY CRASHED, THE SHARES BECOMING VALUELESS.

OLD FAMILY FRIEND DUNSTAN WOOD WAS THERE TO HELP AND ADVISE.

THERE WAS ALSO THE QUESTION OF **HOW** HIS FATHER HAD DIED. HE HAD BEEN 'SOMETHING IN THE CIVIL SERVICE', BUT HAD NEVER DISCUSSED IT WITH HIS SON.

THESE WERE MATTERS BLAKE INTENDED TO LOOK INTO.

BUT FIRST, THERE WAS THE MINISTER. AND THE MAN HE HAD COME TO BOSNIA TO KILL.

OH! YOU'VE GOT THE SAME BIRTHDAY AS ME!

Bilmira

WE'RE BOTH SCORPIOS.

THE OLDEST TRICK IN THE BOOK.

MAYBE WE CAN GET TOGETHER LATER AND SEE WHAT ELSE WE HAVE IN COMMON, MISS... ?

BILMIRA MEGARA.

MAYBE.

OUR AGENT REPORTS BLAKE HAS ARRIVED IN SARAJEVO, SIR.

I ARRANGE FOR HIS EDUCATION TO BE PAID FOR. I TREAT HIM LIKE MY OWN SON. AND **THIS** IS HOW HE REPAYS ME.

I DON'T KNOW HOW SARA WILL TAKE HIS DEATH. FIRST LUKE, AND NOW HER SON. I SHALL HAVE TO BE THERE TO **CONSOLE** HER.

WELL...? THE **NEW** DETECTOR?

THE ORDER'S BEEN HELD UP BY THAMES HOUSE, SIR.

PERHAPS WE SHOULD ORDER IT FROM THE GADGET PAGES OF ONE OF YOUR MEN'S MAGAZINES, JUSTIN?

HE *'FLASHED'* HER ROOM, CHECKING EVERYTHING IN IT BEFORE ENTERING.

HE USED *'HALF-MOON STEPPING'* — ALLOWING HIM TO QUICKLY MOVE FROM STANDING TO CROUCHING.

THEY TOLD ME YOU'D BE COMING...

... AND WHAT TO DO.

'THAT DEPENDS ENTIRELY ON YOU, OLD MAN, YOU KNOW.'

BEFORE THE BUG HAD BEEN DISCOVERED, HE HAD LEARNT A LITTLE ABOUT BILMIRA.

BUT HE DIDN'T KNOW IF SHE WAS DELTA CLASS OR OMEGA CLASS.

IF SHE WAS OMEGA, THERE WOULD BE NO REASONING WITH HER.

OMEGA CLASS COULD ALSO EMIT FREE ELECTRONS — THEY DO NOT REFLECT OR REFRACT LIGHTWAVES, RENDERING THE AGENT INVISIBLE.

AS IT WAS PITCH BLACK, HE COULDN'T KNOW FOR CERTAIN WHICH CLASS SHE WAS IN.

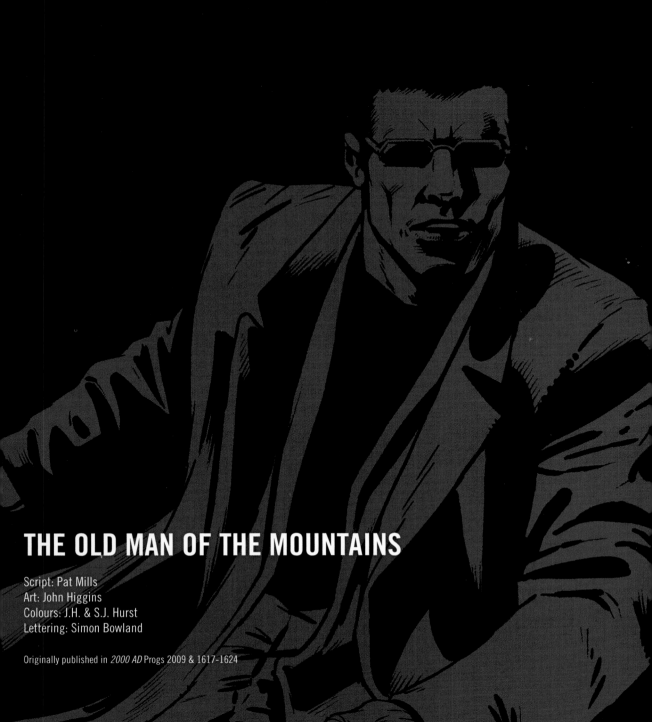

THE OLD MAN OF THE MOUNTAINS

Script: Pat Mills
Art: John Higgins
Colours: J.H. & S.J. Hurst
Lettering: Simon Bowland

Originally published in *2000 AD* Progs 2009 & 1617-1624

HIS *"PRIMAL"* WAS DELIBERATELY TRAUMATIC, SO HE WAS *DISASSOCIATED* FROM FEELING ANY FEAR ON MISSIONS.

THE GUARD DOG WAS A *"STEALTH PIT BULL".* IT'D HAD ITS VOCAL CORDS CUT SO IT DID NOT MAKE ANY SOUND THAT WOULD ALERT AN INTRUDER.

BLAKE HEARD IT PANTING--

HE USED A SHOOTING KNIFE PROPELLED WITH COMPRESSED CO_2.

THANKS TO HIS PRIMAL, 'S FIGHT-OR-FLIGHT RESPONSES WERE TED BY MASSIVE ADRENALINE SURGES...

...TO *SUPERHUMAN* LEVELS.

I'M AFRAID MURDER HAS NOT HELPED YOUR CHANCES OF GETTING A BRITISH PASSPORT, "MS MEGARA".

BUT I AM AWARE IT WAS SELF-DEFENCE AND I AM MOST IMPRESSED BY YOUR COURAGE.

IF YOU JOIN MY ORGANISATION, I CAN GET YOU OFF THAT REFUGEE SHIP.

YOU CAN BEGIN A NEW LIFE IN THE WEST AS A BRITISH CITIZEN.

SO WHERE'S CATCH.

MY DEAR MS MEGARA!

I'M AN OLD MAN.

SO ALL THE DOCTORS HAD TO DO WAS INTENSIFY AND SEPARATE YOUR PERSONALITIES: TANYA LATEKA AND BILMIRA MEGARA.

EXCUSE ME...ALL?

RIGHT.

TO CREATE MASSIVE ADRENALINE SURGES IN YOU.

THAT FEELING I HAVE ALL THE TIME.

BUTTERFLIES IN MY STOMACH.

YES... MY FIRST MISSION...

IT'S AN *EXCHANGE JOB* FOR OUR AMERICAN FRIENDS, BILMIRA. WE DO ONE FOR THEM, THEY DO ONE FOR US.

WE WANT YOU TO TAKE OUT AN AMERICAN INDIAN MINISTER OF CULTURE WHO IS BEING RATHER... *DIFFICULT.*

HE SEEMS TO HAVE FORGOTTEN THEY'RE A *DEFEATED* NATION.

A MINING CORPORATION WANTS TO START WORK ON THE RESERVATION. IT MEANS DIGGING UP A TRADITIONAL INDIAN BURIAL GROUND.

WELL, WE CAN'T STAND IN THE WAY OF PROGRESS, CAN WE?

DRIVING UP ON TO THE MESA, IT SEEMED TO HER LIKE A GIANT PRISON WITHOUT BARS.

NO TOURISTS WERE ALLOWED IN CERTAIN SECTORS, SUPPOSEDLY TO PROTECT THE INDIANS.

NO ALCOHOL WAS PERMITTED. THE PEOPLE NO LONGER FARMED. THEY SPENT THEIR DAYS MAKING DOLLS OR WATCHING TELEVISION.

ALTHOUGH THEY SAID NOTHING, THEIR EYES TOLD HER WHAT THEY THOUGHT OF THE WHITE MAN.

THE MINISTER OF CULTURE HAD A DIFFICULT JOB. HE WAS SEEN AS A TRAITOR BY THE TRADITIONAL TRIBAL COUNCIL OF ELDERS...

...AND A "PROBLEM" BY THE MINERAL COMPANY FOR REFUSING TO LET THEM STRIP-MINE.

THEY HAD NOT LOST LIKE THE GERMANS OR THE JAPANESE FOR TWENTY YEARS.

THEY HAD LOST *FOREVER.*

HOW CAN I HELP YOU, MS MEGARA?

THE ORIGINAL OLD MAN OF THE MOUNTAINS, AL-HASSAN, HAD USED **OPIATES** TO HELP HIS KILLERS WITHSTAND PAIN.

DUNSTAN WOOD'S MEDICAL TEAM INJECTED HIS GREYSUITS WITH **SYNTHETIC NARCOTICS** TO ENSURE LONG-TERM IMMUNITY TO PAIN.

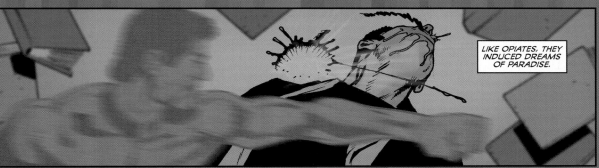

LIKE OPIATES, THEY INDUCED DREAMS OF PARADISE.

THEY REMOVED THEIR **MORALITY,** SO AGENTS COULD KILL WITHOUT MOTIVE, EMOTION OR REMORSE...

...AND CREATED A ~~CAL~~ **DEPENDENCY** ~~~~ THEIR SUPPLIER.

ONLY BLAKE HAD KICKED THE HABIT.

THE KID FROM THE COUNCIL ESTATE VERSUS THE PUBLIC-SCHOOL BOY!

WHO SAYS WE'RE NOT AN **EQUAL OPPORTUNITIES** EMPLOYER?

SHE INVITED HIM BACK TO HER APARTMENT.

THEN HE HEARD HIS MOTHER'S VOICE IN HIS HEAD:

"‹HAVE NOTHING TO DO WITH **WOMEN**, SON! THEY'RE ALL GOOD-FOR-NOTHING TRAMPS!›

"‹THE TROUBLE IN THIS WORLD BEGAN WITH EVE AND THAT'S HOW IT WILL END! **EVE** STARTED IT AND **SHE** WILL END IT!›"

...HER ORDERED HIM TO ...ENCE THE LAMB"...

...AND WASH AWAY HIS SINS WITH HER **BLOOD**.

IT SEEMED TO **"THE SILENCER OF THE LAMBS"** THAT IF HE KILLED BLAKE NOW, THE OLD MAN WOULD OVERLOOK HIS RECENT FAILURES.

ESPECIALLY IF HE SAVED THE OLD MAN'S LIFE.

HAD BOUGHT A LETTER
ADY HAMILTON TO NELSON
ADVERTISED IT ON EBAY.

UNSTAN WOOD COULDN'T RESIST IT AND THUS
LAKE DISCOVERED HIS ADDRESS: A PENTHOUSE
APARTMENT OVERLOOKING NELSON DOCK.

THERE WERE GREYSUITS ON
GUARD OUTSIDE THE BUILDING.

AFTER THE MINISTER'S
EXECUTION, THIS WAS
TO BE EXPECTED.

THERE WERE SO MANY
REASONS WHY DUNSTAN
WOOD, TOO, HAD TO DIE.

OOD'S DEPARTMENT PAYING
PUBLIC-SCHOOL EDUCATION.

HE HAD **PAID**,
ALL RIGHT...

...IN A CAGE, WITH SNAKES AND
VENOMOUS SPIDERS, COURTESY
OF DOCTOR GREEN.

SHE HAD REGRESSED HIM TO EARLY
CHILDHOOD BECAUSE "IT'S IMPORTANT TO
TRAUMATISE THE SUBJECT **BEFORE** HE HAS
FULLY DEVELOPED HIS EGO STATE".

LATER FOR
DOCTOR GREEN.

THEN THERE WAS HIS **FATHER**--"SOMETHING IN THE CIVIL SERVICE"--WHO HAD MYSTERIOUSLY DIED WHEN HE WAS A BOY.

HIS MOTHER'S **INVESTMENTS** SUDDENLY BECAME WORTHLESS, SO SHE HAD TO TURN TO OLD FAMILY FRIEND WOOD FOR HELP.

SOMEHOW, WOOD WAS CONNECTED WITH BOTH TRAGEDIES.

ABOVE ALL, HE OWED HIS BOSS FOR THAT **OTHER** OLD MAN...

...WHO HAD DENOUNCED BRITAIN ON HIS SATELLITE PROGRAMME FOR STEALING HIS COUNTRY'S RICHES. WOOD HAD SENT BLAKE TO EXECUTE HIM.

A GOOD